THIS BOOK BELONGS TO

ANGEL THE PUG BASKETBALL ABC BOOK

by Wilheimina Long and Wellington J. Williams Jr

This book is published by Jellybeans Children's Books Publishing Inc. January 2019

www.RayTheBuffalo.com

ISBN: 978-0-9896596-7-3 • Printed in USA

MEET ANGEL THE PUG

ANGEL the Pug is smart and loves to go for walks where she makes lot of friends. She enjoys playing with her basketball toy. Her favorite foods are chicken, spaghetti, eggs, and broccoli. At times, she prefers vegetables over meat. Her favorite snack is Cheerios. Check out Angel's ears. She loves to lift her left ear, and it's incorporated into her logo. Angel is so cute and so lovable! ANGEL the Pug's motto is: LET'S GO

Angel

A
ANGEL'S ABCs

is for
ATHLETES

is for
BASKETBALL

is for COURT

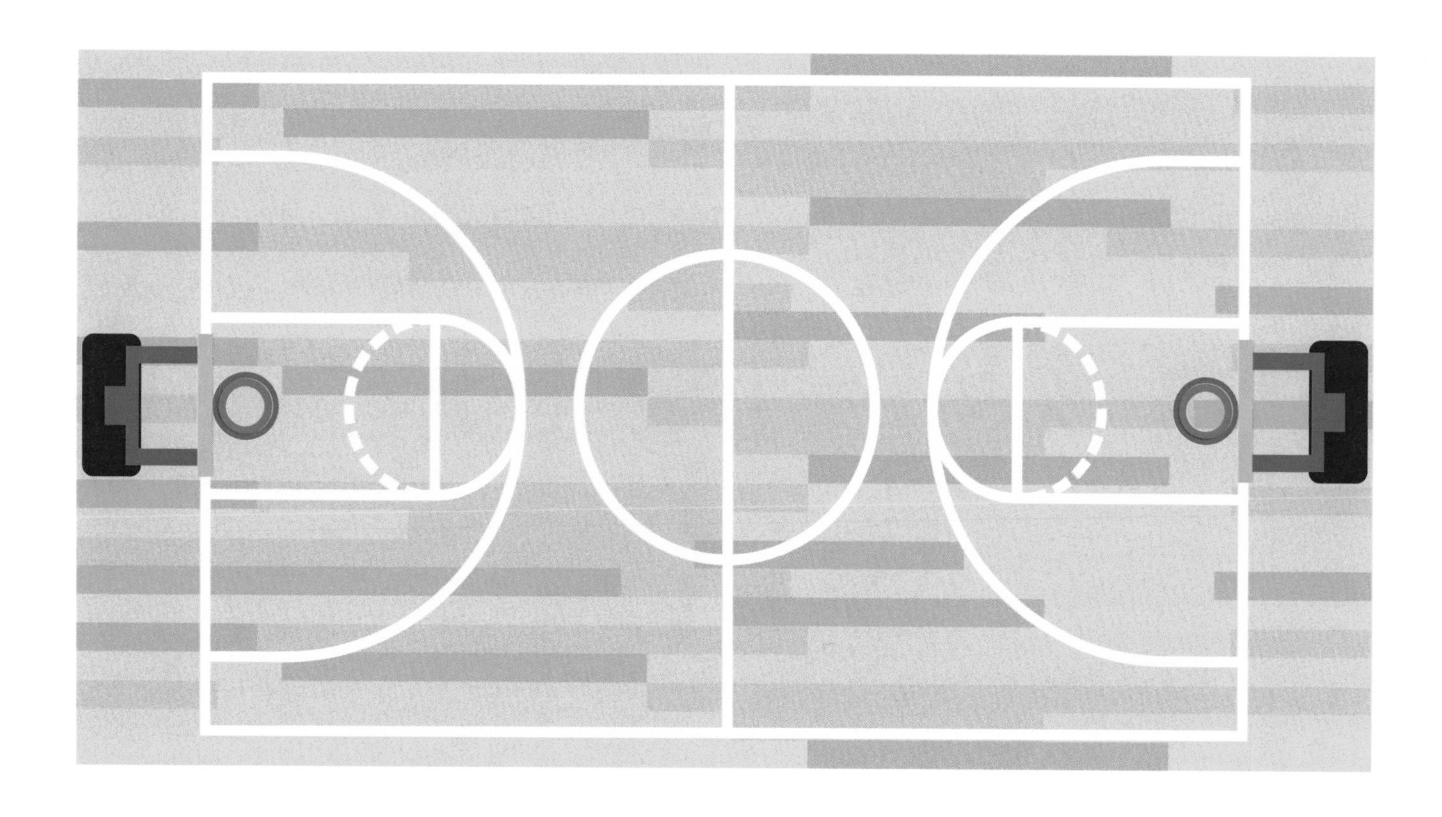

is for
DRIBBLE

is for
EAT HEALTHY

is for
FLOOR

is for
GAME CLOCK

is for
HOOP

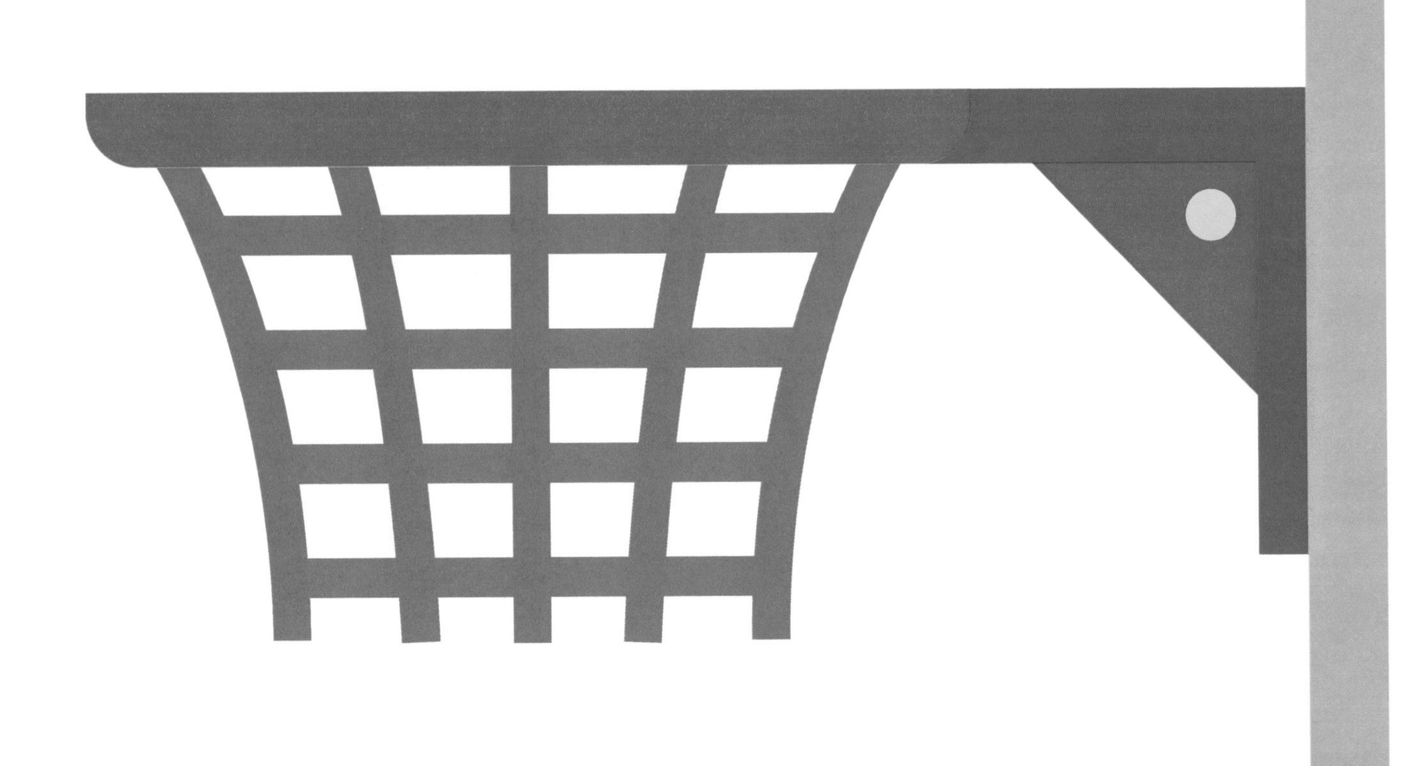

is for INTERNATIONAL WHEELCHAIR BASKETBALL

is for
JERSEY

is for KEY

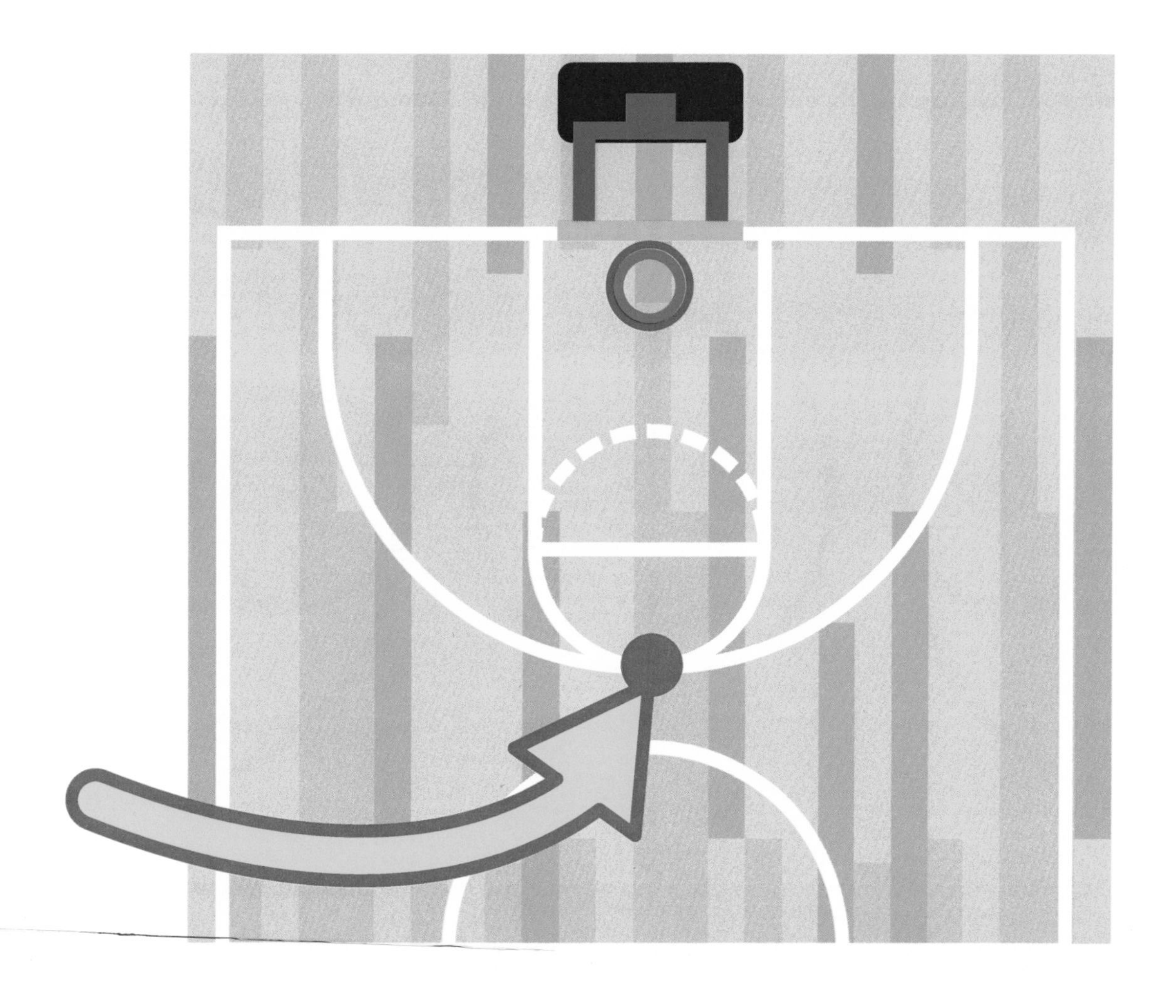

is for
LINES

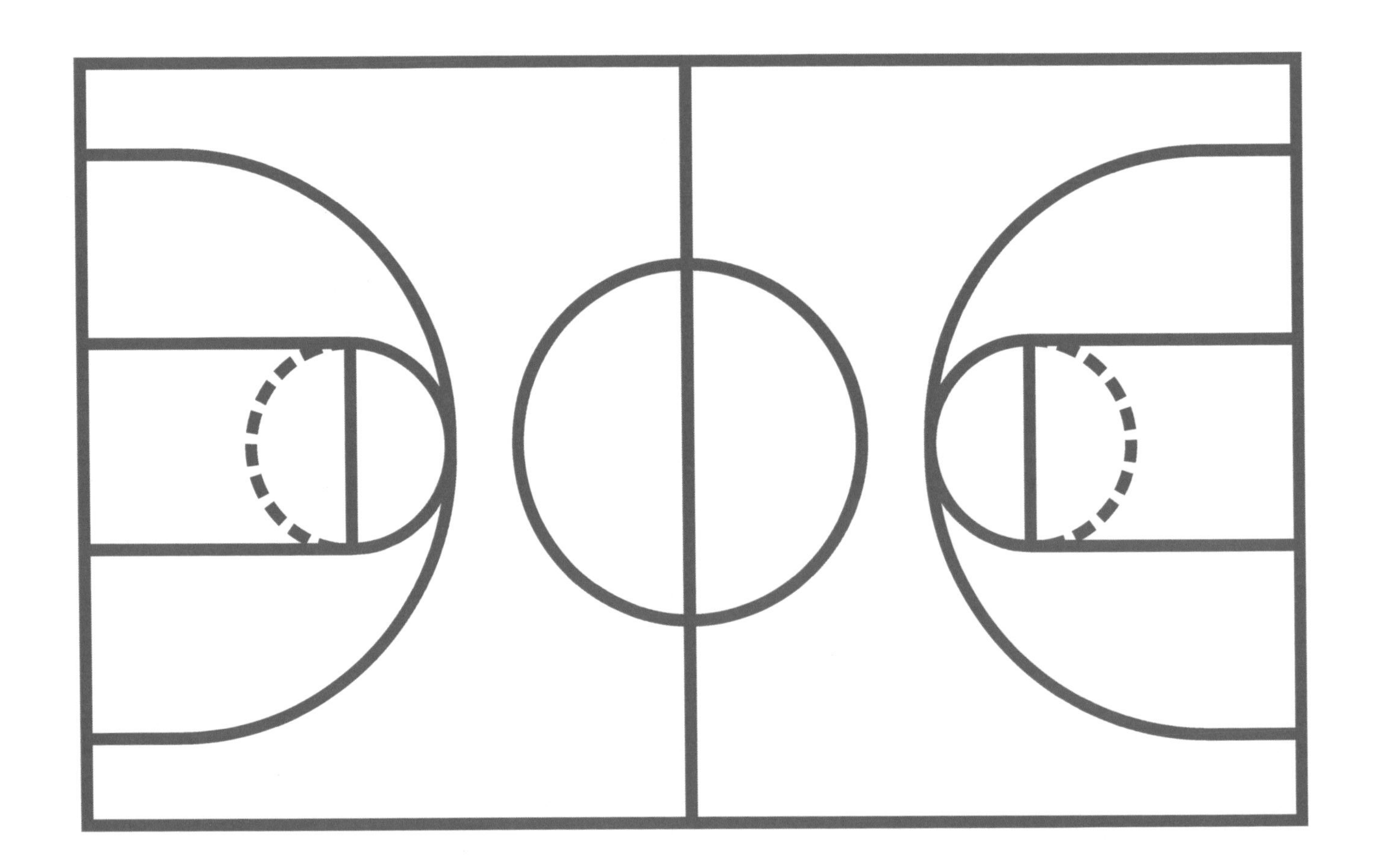

is for
MID-LINE
COURT

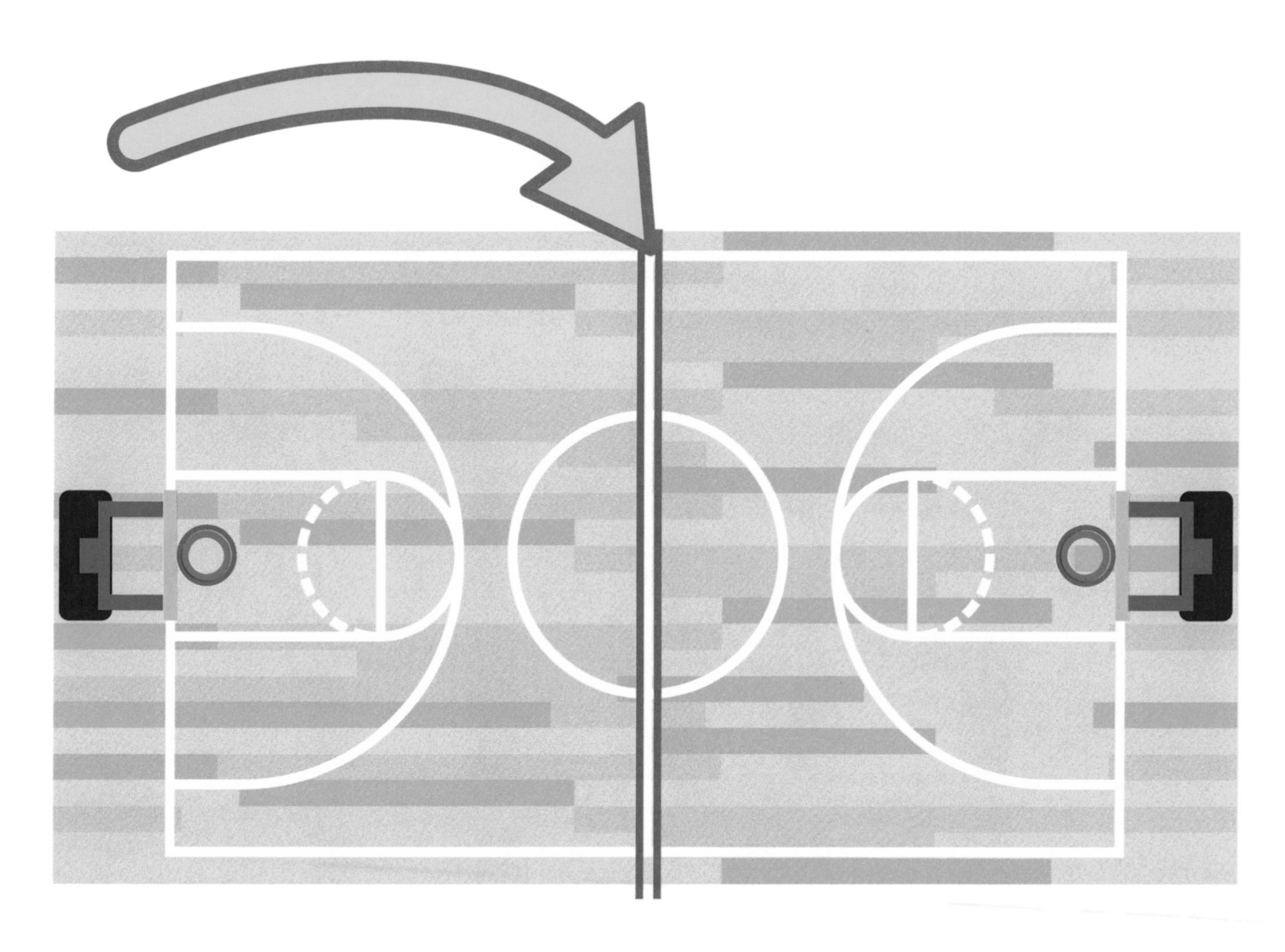

is for
NET

is for
OFFENSE

Pp is for PLAY

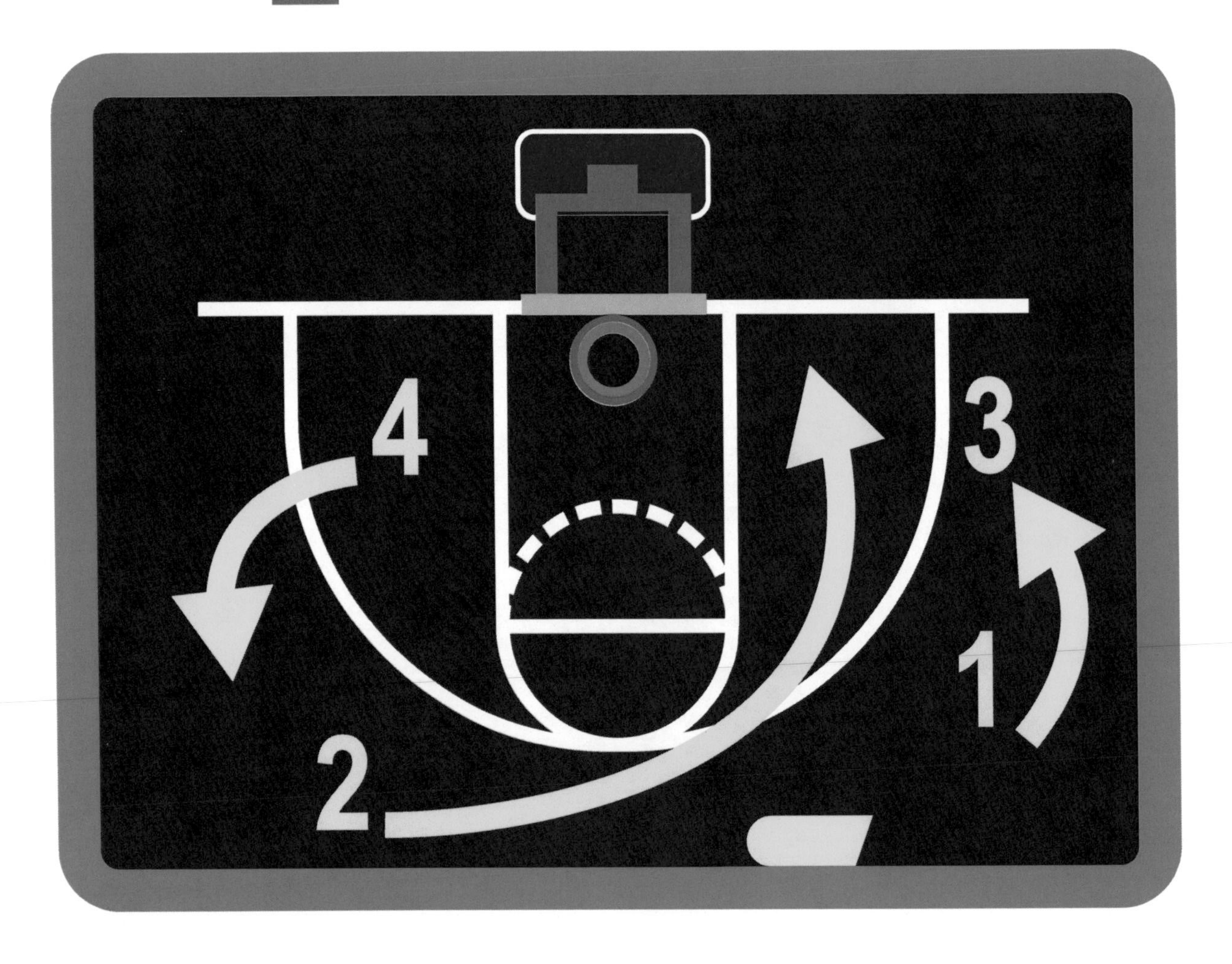

is for QUARTERS

is for
REFEREE

is for STOPWATCH

is for TIMEOUT

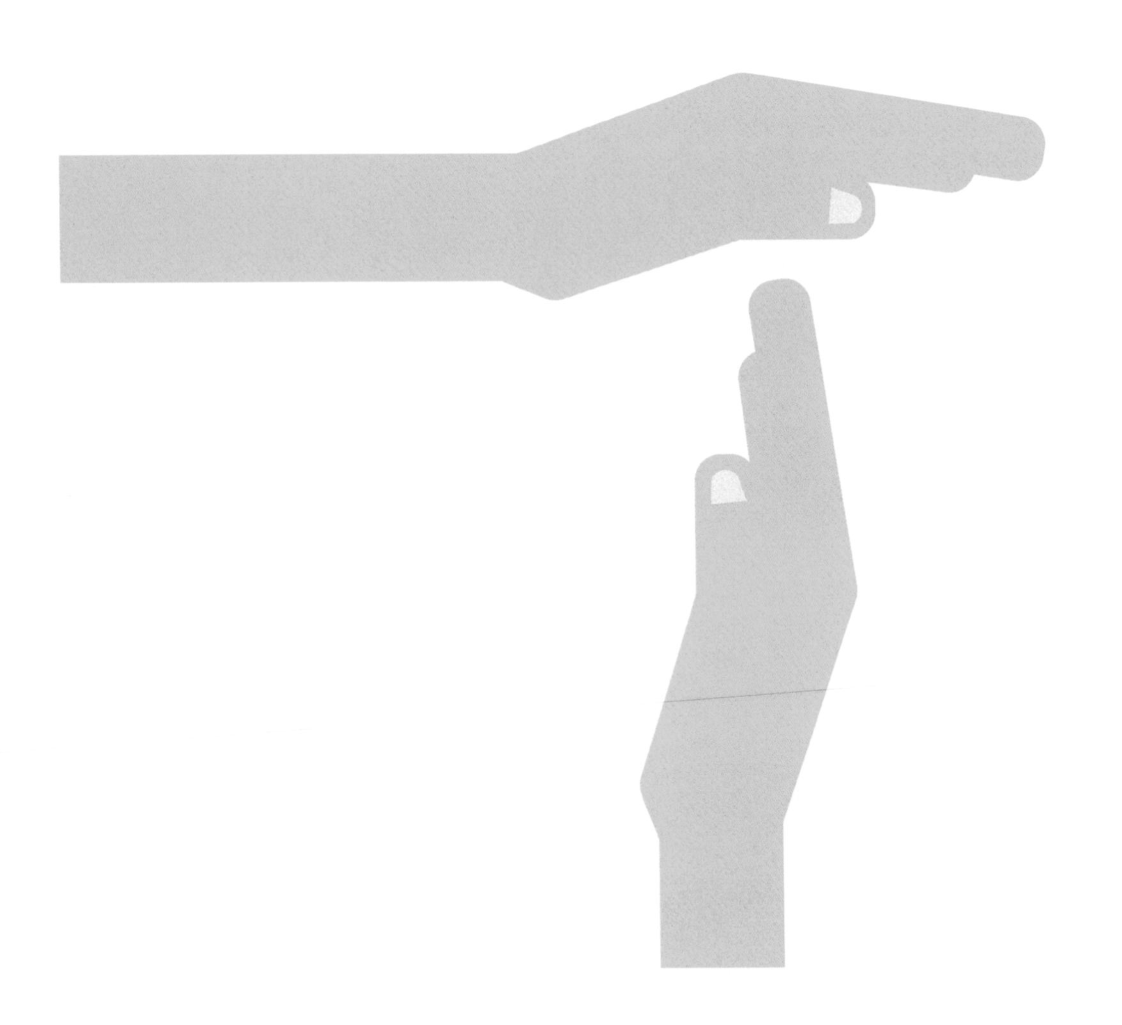

is for
UNIFORM

Vv
is for
VICTORY

is for
WATER BOTTLE

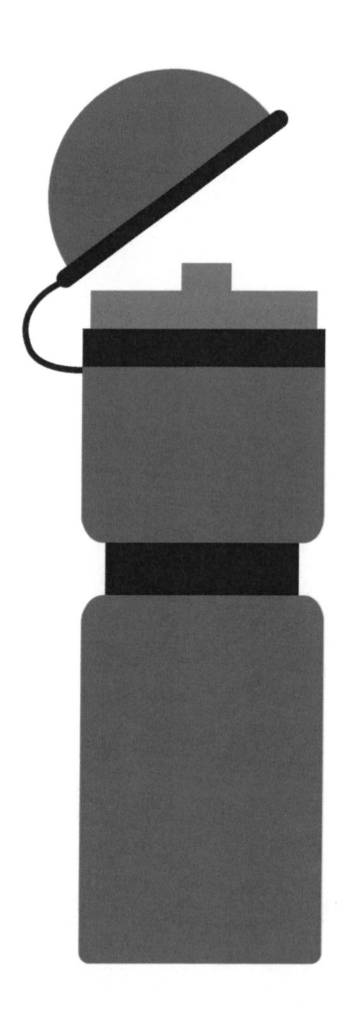

is for
X IN A PLAY

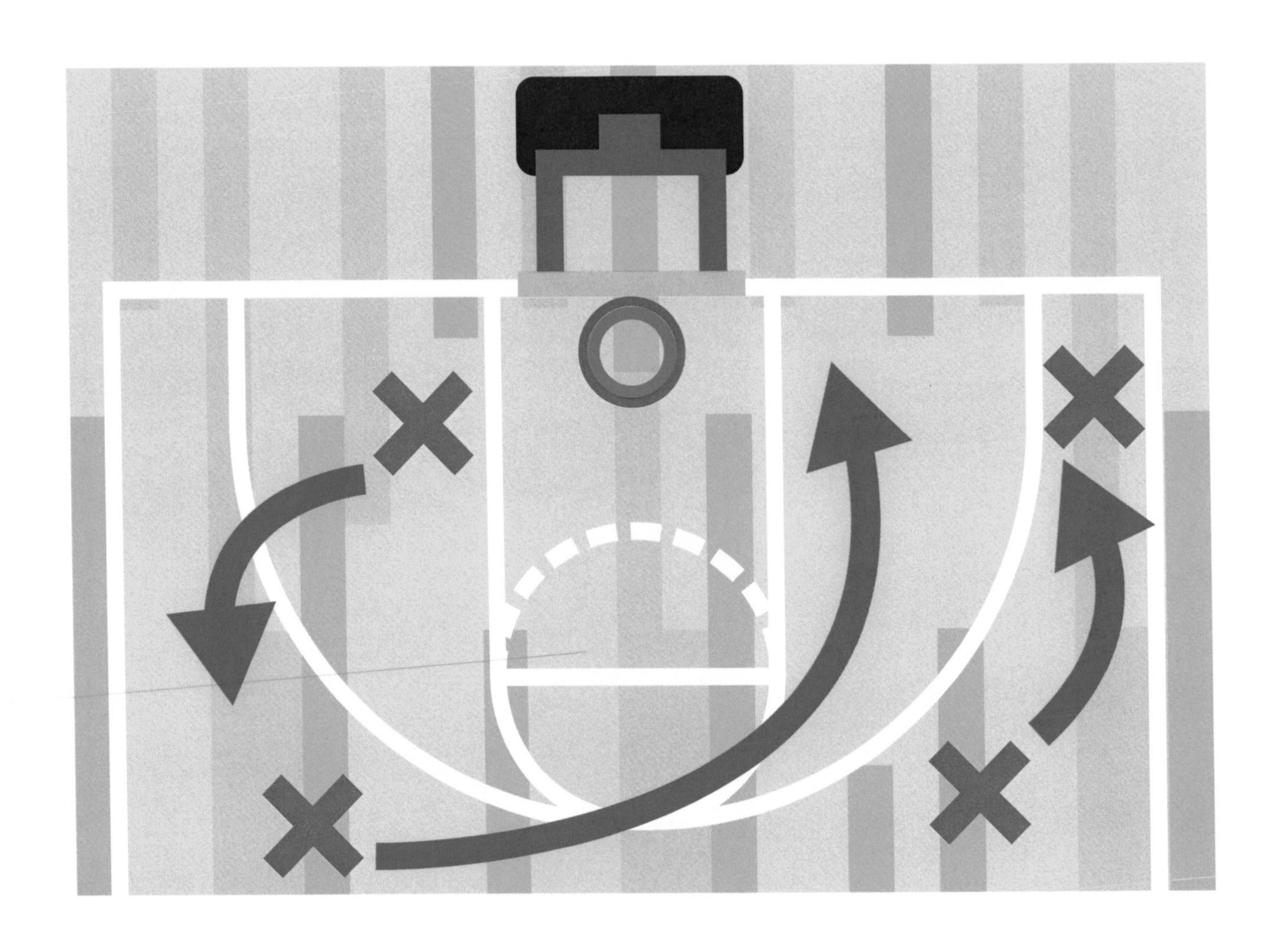

is for
YELLOW SOCKS

Zz is for ZONE

COLORING FUN!

AUTHORS & DESIGNER

WILHEIMINA LONG

Wilheimina is a children's book author, entreprenuer, graphic designer, and fine artist who enjoys painting portraits. She received her B.A. degree from the University of Mary Washington. Wilheimina has always been an advocate for children and she founded in 1999 the non-profit, Youth Matter Inc. Creating what is the Ray the Buffalo & Friends book series is her passion, as her desire is to motivate and encourage children to be their best and to always strive to excel. She personally produced the layout and design of all books in the series. She continues to work toward her entrepreneur goals with her creative services agency BRITLON. www.britlon.com

WELLINGTON J. WILLIAMS JR

Wellington J. Williams Jr currently serves as a Program Manager in support of the US Navy. His career experience includes significant roles in all aspects of resourcing and acquisition for various naval programs. He has a B.S. degree in Civil Engineering from Colorado State University. He had an outstanding military career where he retired at the rank of Commander, US Navy. In his free time, you will find him mentoring youth and young adults and enjoying the beach with his fur buddy Angel the Pug.

WWW.RAYTHEBUFFALO.COM

Visit with us online to purchase items from the Ray the Buffalo & Friends series, to include other books, stickers, prints, bookmarks, buttons, and other cool stuff.

Meet the other friends of Ray the Buffalo there.